Key Stage 1

History

Written by H. Foote and J. Keys

Published by Prim-Ed Publishing

Foreword

This series of books provides teachers with a wide variety of activities which will give their pupils the opportunity to develop an awareness of the past and the ways in which it is different from the present.

The materials can be used to support a whole class theme or by groups or individual pupils for their research.

The activities cover all 'Areas of Study' in the Key Stage 1 curriculum and develop the 'Key Elements'.

Contents

National Curriculum Reference Chart

Page Title	Pg	Areas of Study				Key Elements								
		1a	1b	2	3	1a	1b	2a	2b	2c	3a	4a	4b	5a
Sing a Song of Sixpence	1		•		•		•	•			•			
Ring-a-Ring o' Roses	2		•		•		•	•			•			
My School Day	3	•				•	•							
Personal Timeline	4	•				•							•	•
Royal Family Tree	5	•		•		•					•	•		•
My Family Tree	6	•				•					•	•	•	
Family Life	7		•					•		•	•		•	
Interview Sheet - World War II	8	•						•	•			•	•	
Interview Sheet - School Days	9	•						•	•			•	•	
Changing With Age	10	•				•							•	•
Time Changes	11	•	•			•				•		•		
Artefacts - 1	12	•	•								•	•	•	•
Artefacts - 2	13	•	•								•	•	•	•
Now and Then - Shopping	14	•	•				•			•			•	
Now and Then - The Office	15	•	•				•			•			•	
Now and Then - The Kitchen	16	•	•				•			•			•	
Now and Then - Getting About	17	•	•				•			•			•	
Now and Then - Games and Toys	18	•	•				•			•			•	
Days of the Week	19	•				•	•							
Months of the Year	20	•				•	•							
Now and Then - Buildings	21	•	•						•			•	•	
Changes in Three Generations - 1	22	•	•			•			•	•		•	•	
Changes in Three Generations - 2	23	•	•			•			•	•		•	•	
Which is Older?	24	•	•			•			•	•		•	•	•
Which is Older? - Clothes	25	•	•			•			•	•		•	•	•
Petra	26				•					•		•	•	
The Great Pyramids of Ancient Egypt	27				•					•		•	•	
The Parthenon	28				•					•	•	•	•	
Stonehenge	29			•	•					•	•	•	•	
Warwick Castle	30			•	•					•	•	•	•	
Three Queens - 1	31	•	•	•		•		•	•	•				•
Three Queens - 2	32	•	•	•		•		•	•	•				
Three Queens - 3	33	•	•	•		•		•	•	•				
Saints' Day	34			•										
When Did They Happen?	35				•			•			•	•		•
Mary Jane Seacole	36			•		•		•	•		•	•		
Neil Armstrong	37			•		•		•	•		•	•		
Helen Sharman	38			•		•		•	•		•	•		
Shakespeare	39			•		•		•	•		•	•		
Roald Dahl	40			•		•		•	•		•	•		
Transporting Goods	41	•	•			•	•							•
Transporting People	42	•	•			•	•							•
People Timeline	43	•	•	•		•	•							•
The Olympic Games	44				•			•	•	•				

Sing a Song of Sixpence

Can you fill in the missing words of this rhyme?

Sing a song of sixpence
A ____________ full of rye
Four and twenty blackbirds
Baked in a ____________.
When the pie was opened
The ____________ began to sing
Wasn't that a dainty ____________
To set before the King?
The King was in his counting ____________
Counting out his ____________
The Queen was in the parlour 
Eating ____________ and honey
The maid was in the ____________
Hanging out the clothes
When down came a ______________
And ____________ off her nose.

Where does this funny song come from?
Well, Charles I was the King of England a long time ago. He loved pies. He also loved surprises! A pie was baked for him which actually contained 24 live blackbirds. (They were put in after the rest of the pie had been cooked.)

Which words in the rhyme tell you that it was composed quite a long time ago?

____

____

____

Ring-a-Ring o' Roses

Ring-a-ring-o' roses
A pocket full of posies
Atishoo, atishoo
We all fall down

No-one is sure where this rhyme came from. Some people say it was written at the time of the Black Death. Many years ago the Black Death was a deadly disease. Many of those who died were left to rot in the street. The streets were very smelly!

1. Why do you think they have 'atishoo, atishoo' in the rhyme?

____

____

2. What would 'all fall down' mean? ______________________________

____

____

3. What do you think posies were? ______________________________

____

4. What do you think the posies were used for? ______________________________

____

____

My School Day

Can you cut out these pictures and put them in the correct order?

What do you usually do **before** morning playtime?________________

____

What do you usually do **after** lunch time?______________________

____

Personal Timeline

My name is ______________________. I am________ years old.

	I was one year old.	I was two years old.	I was three years old.	I was four years old.	I was five years old.
0	1	2	3	4	5

When I was born I could ____

____

When I was one I could ____

____

When I was two I could ____

____

When I was three I could ____

____

When I was four I could ____

____

When I was five I could ____

____

When I was six I could ____

____

Royal Family Tree

This is a part of the family tree for the Royal family.

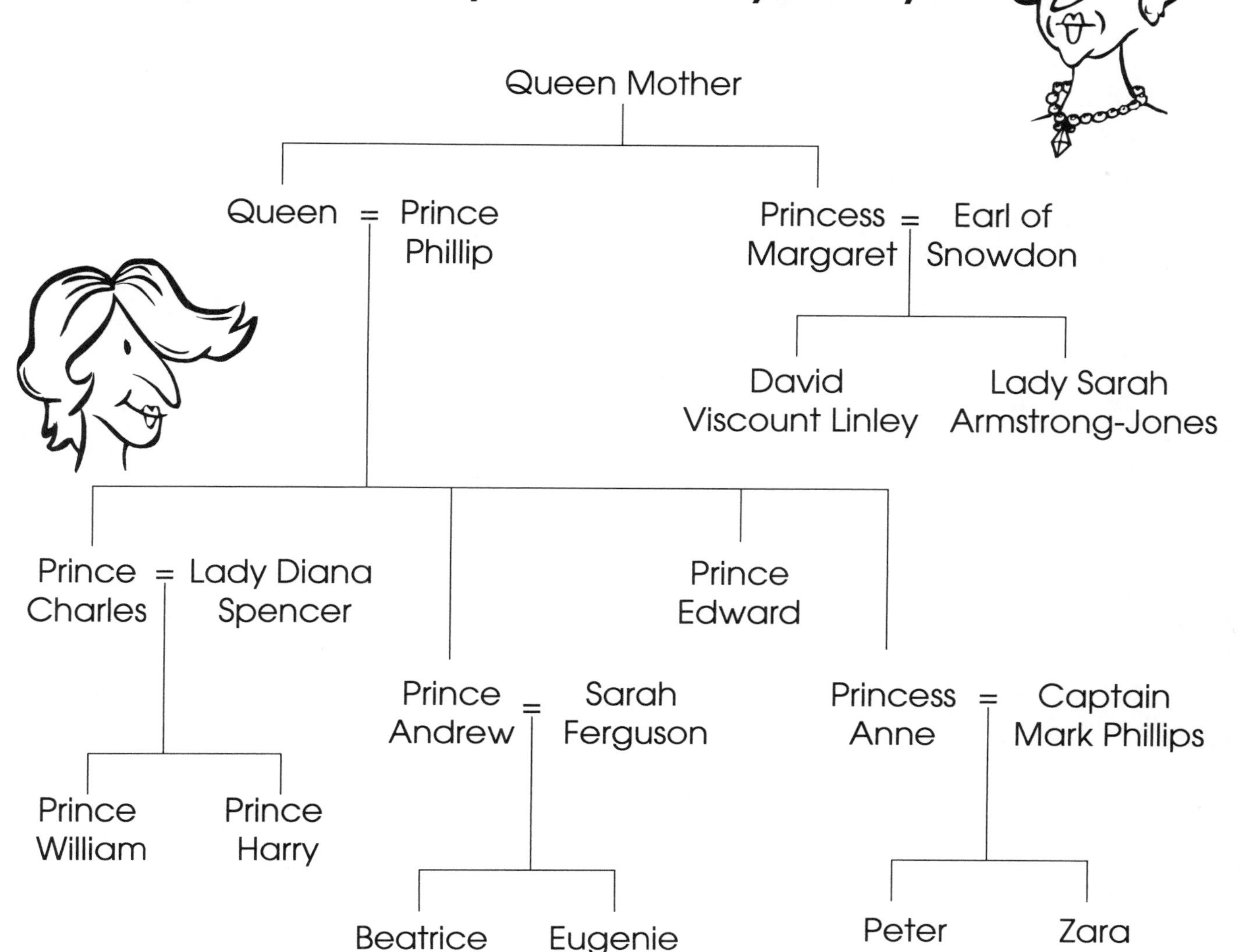

Who is the mother of William? ______________________________

Who is the mother of Anne? ______________________________

Who is the father of Charles? ______________________________

Who is the mother of the Queen? ______________________________

Do Anne and Edward have the same mother? ______________________________

Do Zara and Anne have the same father? ______________________________

Are Peter and Harry brothers? ______________________________

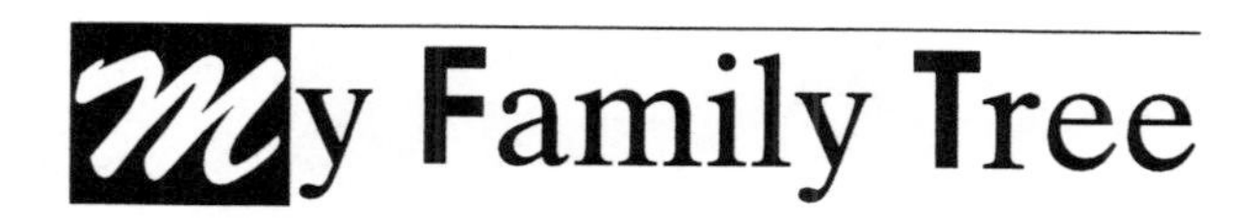

My Family Tree

Can you draw your family tree?

Put yourself and your brothers and sisters in first.

Then put in your parents.

Can you include your grandparents?

Family Life

Look at this picture. It shows a family 100 years ago.

How may adults can you see? ☐

How many children can you see? ☐

Can you see any animals? ☐

Can you see any toys? ☐

How would you describe the clothes they are wearing? ____________

____

____

____

Do you think the people are happy? ____________

____

Interview Sheet - World War II

Talk to someone who lived during World War II.

You can use a tape-recorder to record their answers too.

About how old were you during WW II?____________________

Where were you living?____________________

Were you living with your family?____________________

Did your father have a special job to do?____________________

Did your mother have a special job to do?____________________

How did you feel about the war?____________________

What were the worst things about the war for you?____________________

Do you have any happy memories of that time?____________________

How did you feel when the war was over?____________________

Interview Sheet - School Days

Use this sheet to talk to someone about their school days, in the past. You can use a tape-recorder to record their answers.

About how many years ago did you go to primary school? ________

Where was your school? ________

Did you like your school? ________

What was the best thing about school? ________

____

____

What was the worst thing about school? ________

____

____

Did you have to wear a uniform? ________

____

What were your teachers like? ________

____

____

What did you play in the playground? ________

____

____

Did you have lunch at school? ________

Did you think you would prefer school then or now? ________

____

____

Changing With Age

Find a photograph of yourself as a baby.

Look at it carefully.

Do you look the same as you do today? ______________________

What is different? ______________________

____

What has stayed the same? ______________________

____

Fill in this chart.

	hair colour	eye colour	skin colour	number of teeth	height
different					
same					

If you live to be 70 or 80 years old, what changes do you think will have taken place by then.

____

____

____

Time Changes

Cut out the pictures and put them in order of time. Glue them onto another piece of paper.

Put the oldest one on the left, and the one from the present on the right. **Past** ←——→ **Present**

Artefacts - 1

Look at these pictures of some objects.

How would you describe them - 'new' or 'old'?

Label each one. Write 'new' or 'old' in the small boxes.

What do you think each object is? Can you name each one?

What do you think they are used for?

Write your ideas next to each picture.

Artefacts - 2

Look at these objects from long ago.

Can you draw what we would use today, in the space beside each one?

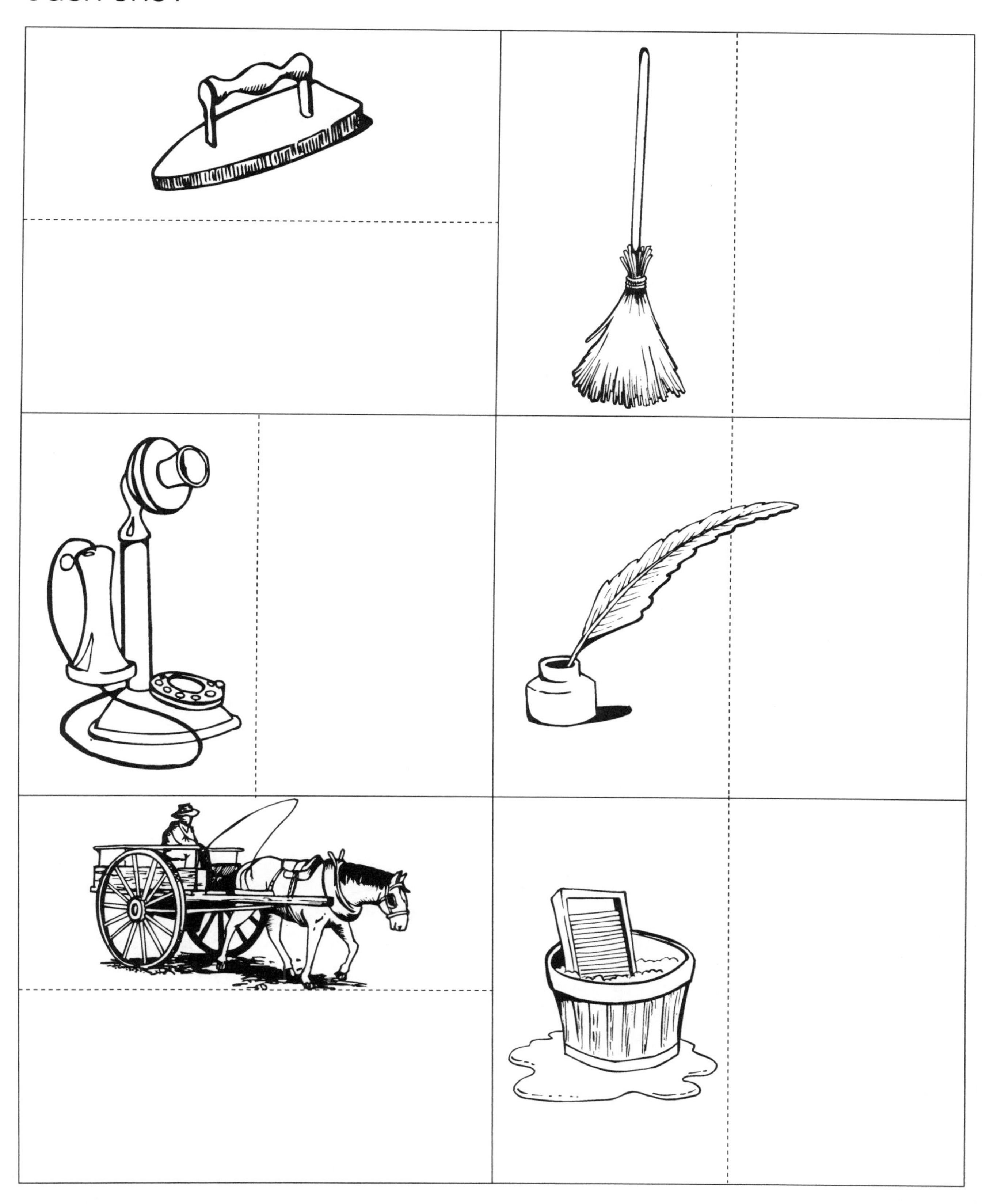

Then and Now - Shopping

Using arrows, can you match these items to the shop in which you think they belong?

One of the differences between these two shops is that people used to have to go to different kinds of shops for each kind of food. Now they can buy all their groceries, their meat and their bread from one shop. It is called a supermarket.

Can you think of any other differences?____________________

____

____

____

Then and Now - The Office

Can you see the differences between these two offices?

You might like to think about the people, the furniture and the machinery.

Write down all the differences you can see and discuss them with a partner.

Then and Now - The Kitchen

Can you see the differences between these two kitchens?

You might like to think about the machinery, the people and what they are doing.

Write down all the differences you can see and discuss them with a partner.

___

___

___

___

___

___

___

___

___

___

___

Which kitchen do you think you would prefer?

Why? ___

___

___

___

Then and Now - Getting About

Before there were engines to drive things, where did the power come from?

Look at each of these pictures and say where the power came from? Can you draw the vehicles we use for these tasks today?

Then and Now - Games and Toys

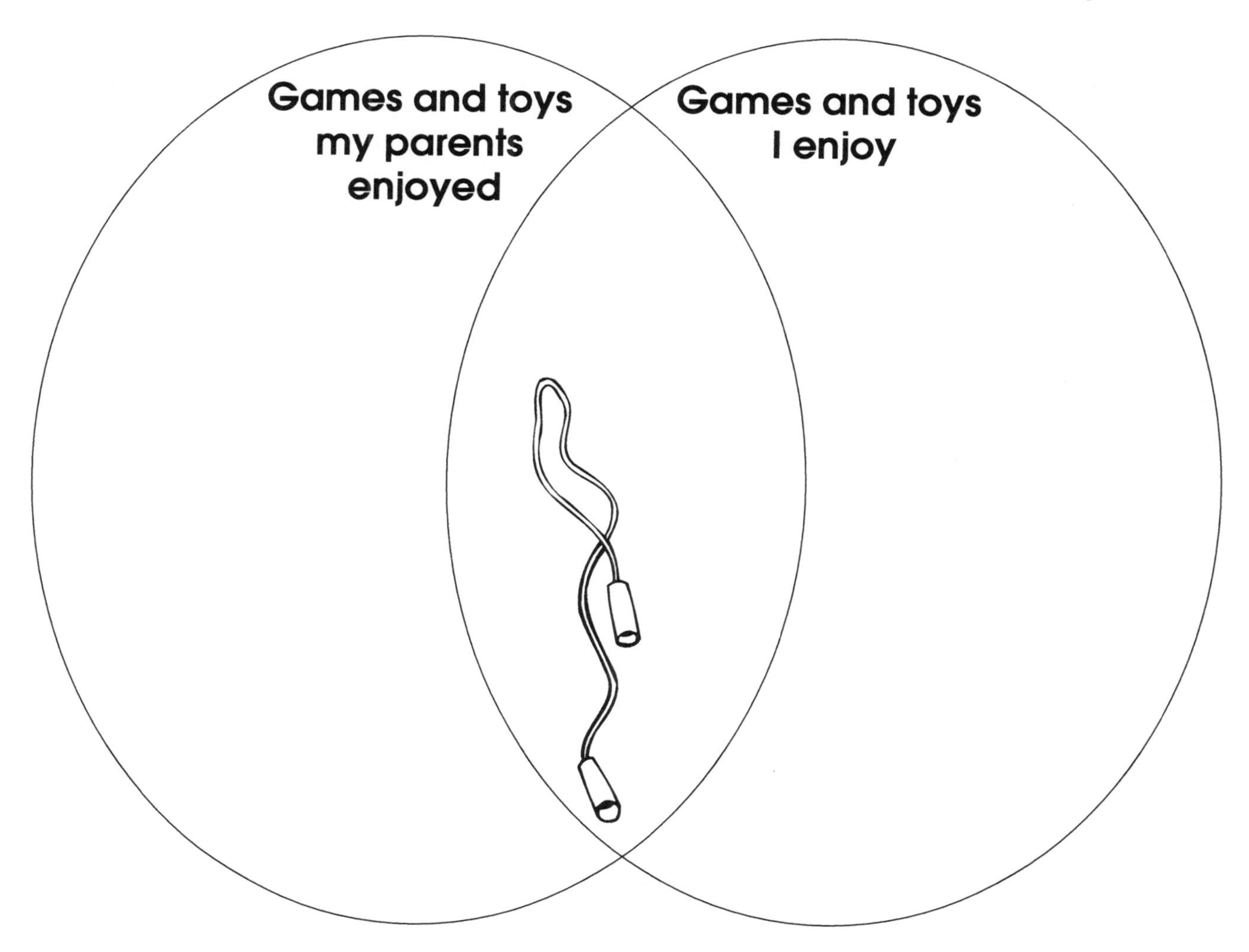

Can you draw these games and toys in the correct place in the diagram?

- skipping rope
- marbles
- chess
- Computer game
- spinning top
- dolls
- ball
- hopscotch
- Russian doll
- wooden train set
- remote control car

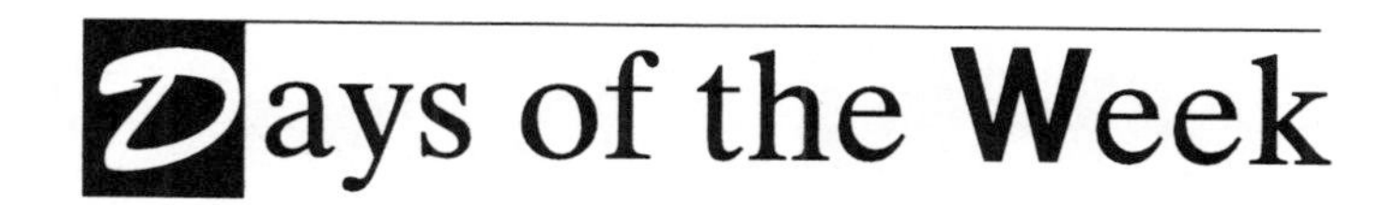

Days of the Week

Can you name the missing days of the week?

Colour the school days one colour.

Colour the two days of the weekend in another colour.

In each segment draw something which happens on that day.

Remember to draw something which happens on that day *each week*. Some ideas are hobbies, clubs, sports.

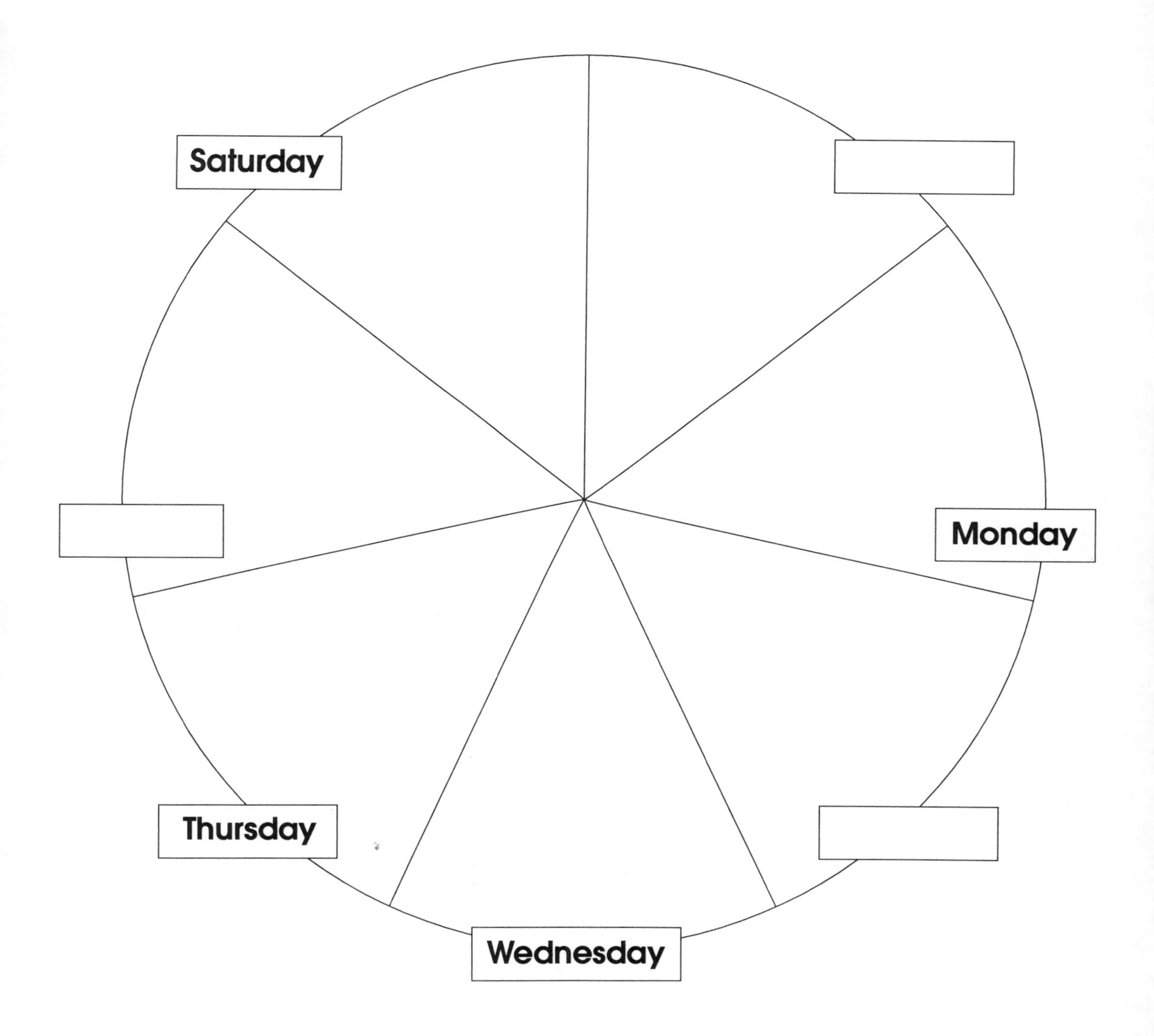

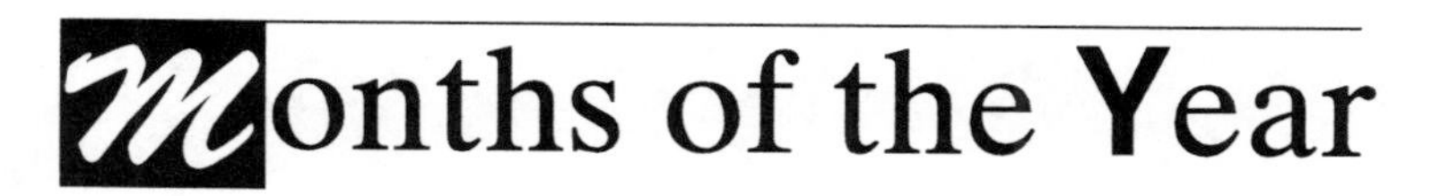

Months of the Year

Calendar

January	**February**		
		July	
	October		

Can you name the missing months of the year?

Can you draw or write in each box, something which happens in that month?

Remember to draw something which happens in that month *each year*. Some ideas are seasons, birthdays, festivals, celebrations.

Then and Now - Buildings

Look at the pictures of these buildings.

What materials were used to build them?

You might like to consider these materials: brick, stone, timber, glass, concrete, plastic, metal, straw, steel, plaster.

Does this help us to find out how old they are?

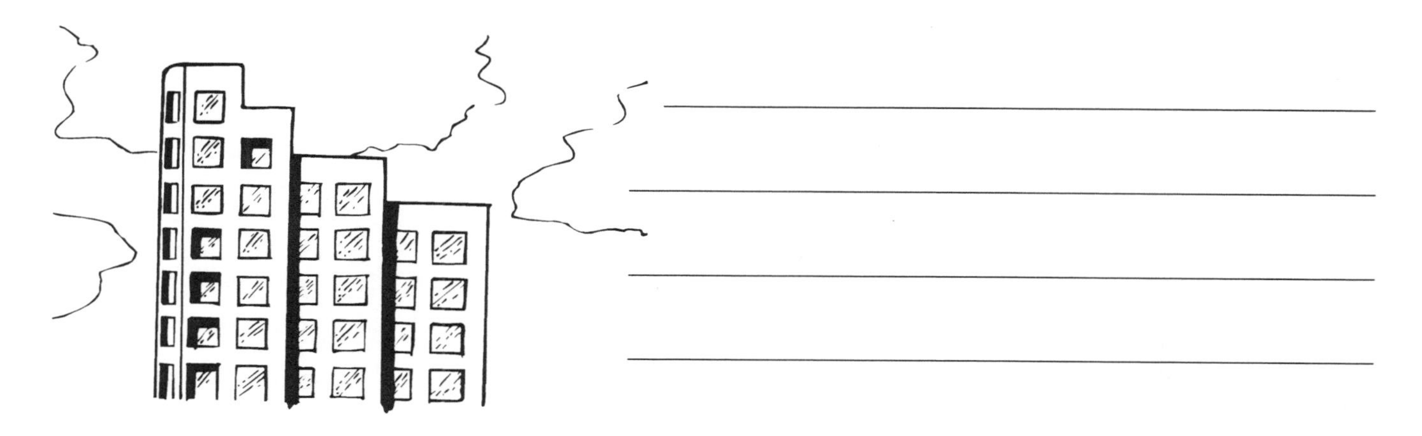

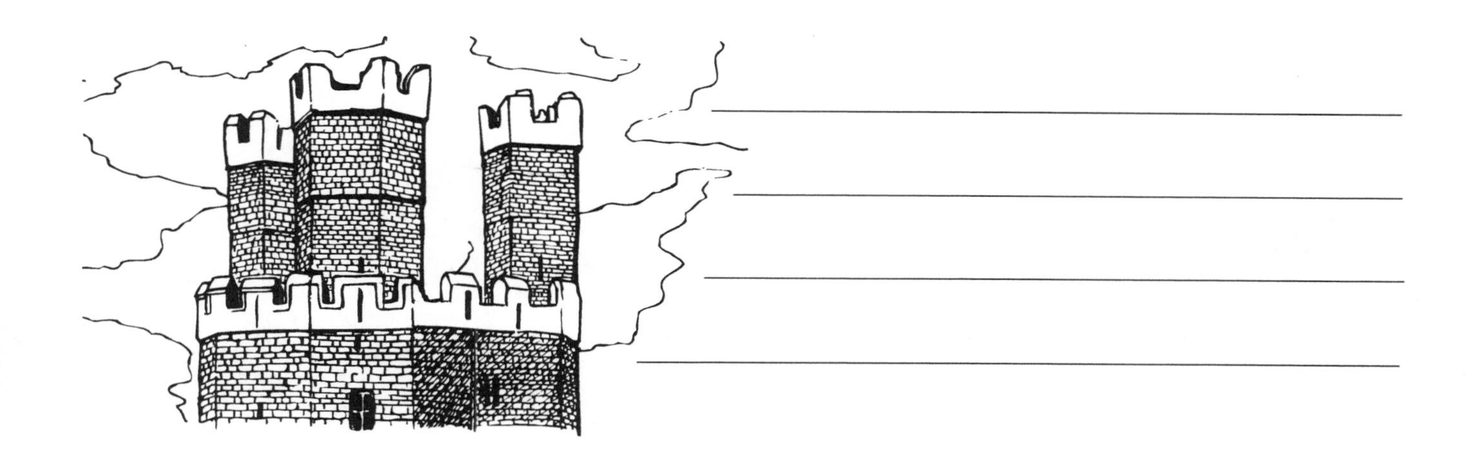

Changes in Three Generations - 1

Look at the pictures on this page.

Do you think they are from your grandparents generation, your parents generation or your generation?

Cut them out and put them where you think they should go in the grid on page 23.

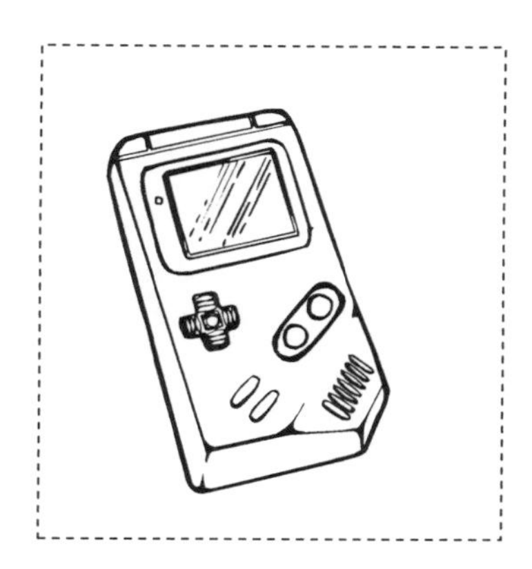

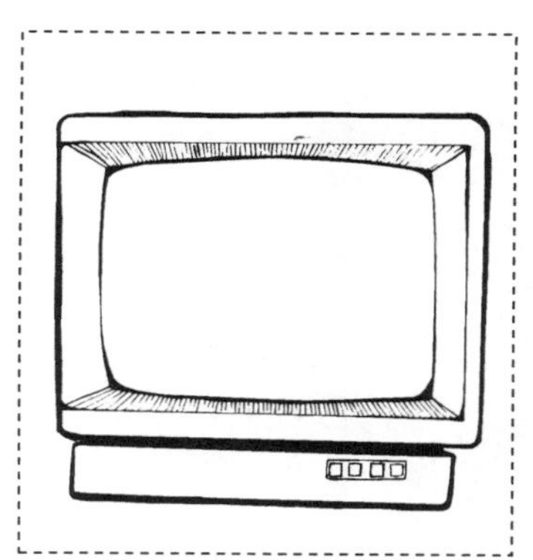

Changes in Three Generations - 2

Place the pictures from page 22 in this grid.

	My Generation	My Parents Generation	My Grandparents Generation
Entertainment			
Clothes			
Transport			

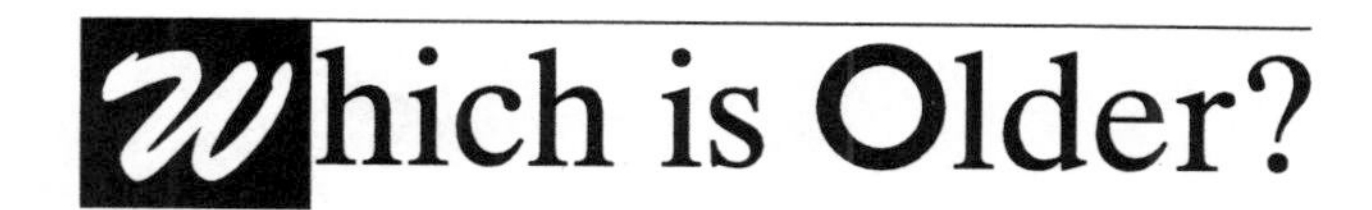

Which is Older?

Look at these pictures.

Draw what you would use now.

Write how the objects have changed and why.

Which is Older? - Clothes

Look at these pictures, do you know which is older in the pair?

Put a tick in the box of the one you think is older.

Write your reason in the other box.

Petra

The city of Petra is in Jordan. The buildings were carved out of the sandstone rocks in the desert. They are more than 2,000 years old.

Use the words at the bottom of the page to complete these sentences.

This building was not built of separate pieces of ________________ or brick.

It is a pink colour because the ________________ is pink.

The building has ________________ and ________________.

It looks almost ________________ in its design.

sandstone	pillars	stone	carvings	symmetrical

The Great Pyramids of Ancient Egypt

The Great Pyramids were built over 4,000 years ago. It took over 20 years to build them. The Sphinx lies in front of the Pyramids to guard them.

Use the words at the bottom of the page to complete these sentences.

The Pyramids are built mainly of ____________________.

The Sphinx was ____________________ out of natural rock.

The Sphinx has a king's ____________________ and a ____________________'s body.

The Pyramids and the Sphinx are ____________________ and parts are missing.

lion	stone	damaged	carved	head

The Parthenon

The Parthenon is a temple which was built in about 420 BC, over 2,400 years ago. It was built for the goddess Athena. There was a room inside for a statue of Athena.

Use the words at the bottom of the page to complete these sentences.

The Parthenon is built of ____________________.

The tall posts are called ____________________.

They held up the roof of the ____________________.

The columns are narrower at the top than the ____________________.

There are ____________________ on the outside of the building.

columns	carvings	stone	bottom	temple

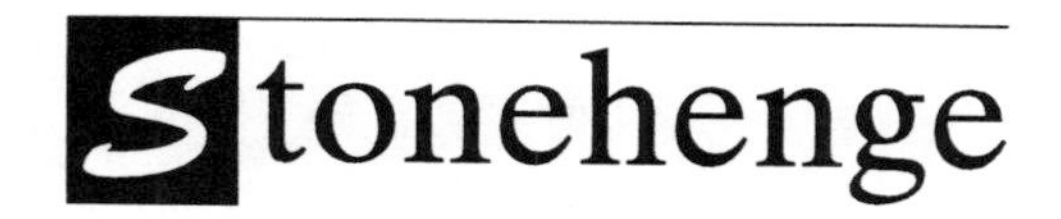

Stonehenge

Stonehenge is a group of very large stones on the Salisbury Plain. The largest stone is 21 feet high. The oldest part of Stonehenge is the outer ditch. Most of the stones we can see today were put in place about 3,500 years ago.

Use the words at the bottom of the page to complete these sentences.

I think Stonehenge would have been ____________________ to build because of the size of the stones.

From this view I can see the remains of an outer ____________________ and an inner ____________________.

The large upright stones have ____________________ lying across them.

From this picture I can see ____________________, so the sun must be shining.

shadows	circle	lintels	difficult	circle

Warwick Castle

Warwick Castle was built over a long period of time. Some stories tell of an important defensive site here in AD 914. However, most of the castle we can see today was built during the Thirteenth Century.

Use the words at the bottom of the page to complete these sentences.

The castle is built mainly of ____________________.

It would have been hard work to lift the stones, because there were no ____________________ long ago.

In this picture I can see three ____________________.

There are ____________________ around the tops of the towers and the walls.

The castle has a dry ____________________ around it.

towers	moat	stone	battlements	cranes

Three Queens - 1

These three queens each reigned for a long time.

Queen Elizabeth II came to the throne in 1952.

How long has she reigned? ____________________

Queen Elizabeth I came to the throne in 1558.
She died in 1603.

How long did she reign? ____________________

Queen Victoria came to the throne in 1837.
She died in 1901.

How long did she reign?____________________

Put a 3 in the box by the Queen who is alive in living memory.
Put a 1 in the box by the Queen who was born first.
Put a 2 in the box by the Queen who lived between these two.

Three Queens - 2

Here are some pictures which show you some of the transport used by the three queens.

Cut out the pictures and put them in the correct box on page 33.

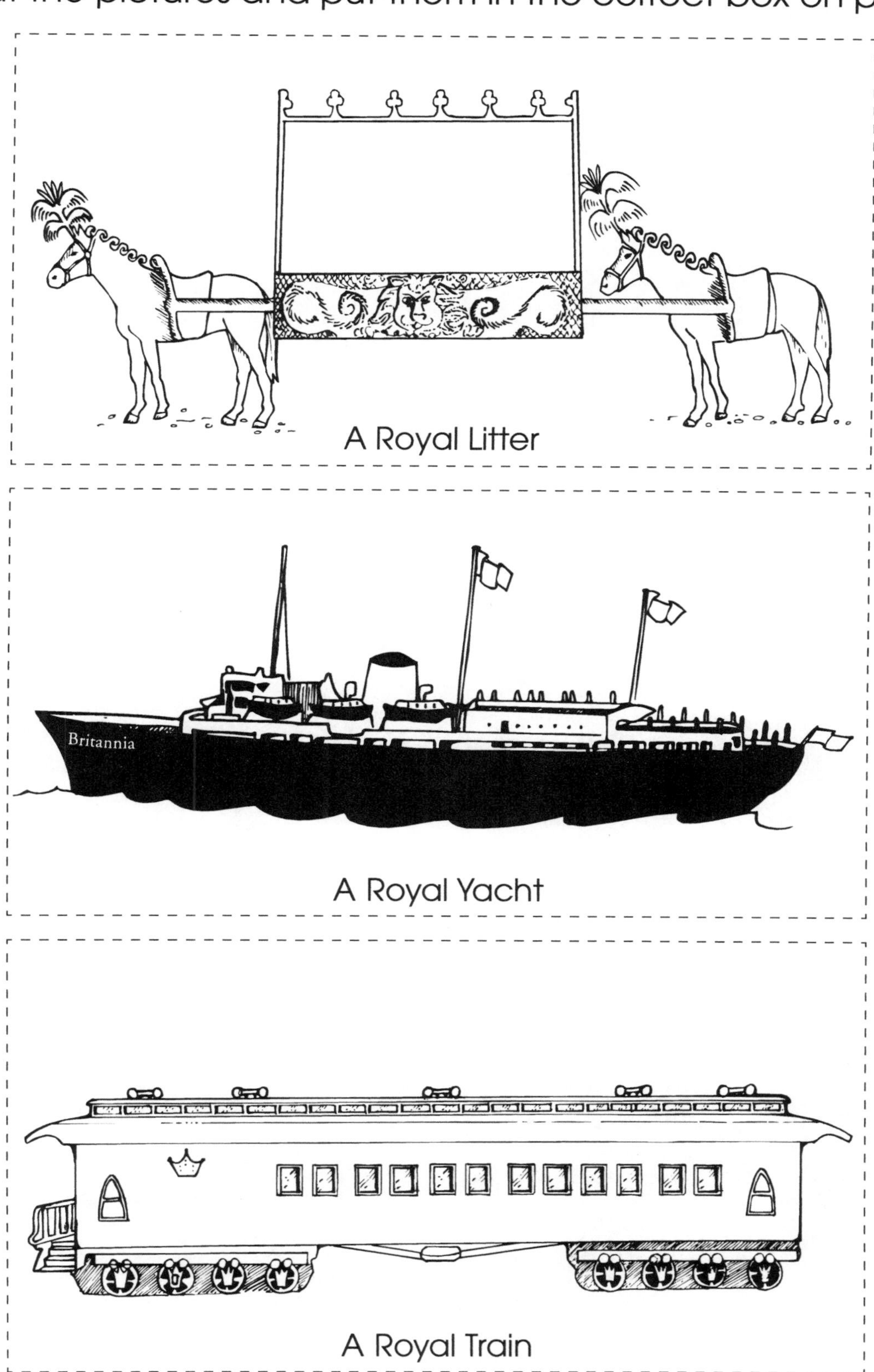

A Royal Litter

A Royal Yacht

A Royal Train

Three Queens - 3

Paste the pictures from page 32 in the correct place on the grid.

	Travel
Queen Elizabeth I	
Queen Elizabeth II	
Queen Victoria	

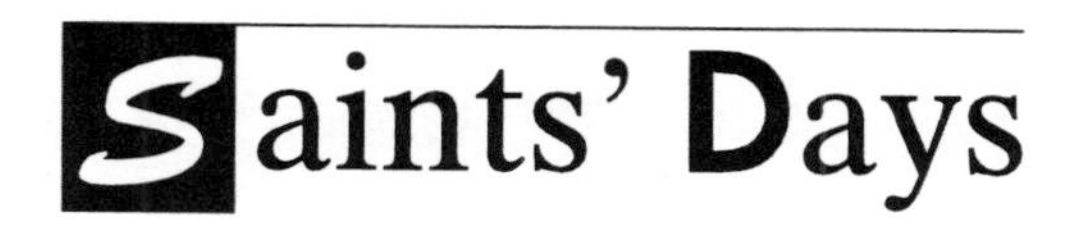

Can you match each of these saints to their days?

When Did They Happen?

Look at each of these events.

Do you think they happened in living memory? Tick the box to say if they happened in living memory or beyond living memory.

How could you check if you are correct? ______________________

____

	In living memory	Beyond living memory
Queen Elizabeth II's coronation.	☐	☐
Fifty years since VE Day.	☐	☐
The death of Queen Victoria.	☐	☐
Queen Elizabeth II's silver jubilee.	☐	☐
The end of World War 1.	☐	☐

Mary Jane Seacole

These statements and pictures tell us something of Mary Jane Seacole's life. Can you match the pictures to the statements.

Mary Jane learned about nursing from her mother, in Jamaica.

Mary Jane nursed the soldiers wounded in the war.

Mary Jane made a special medicine to help cure cholera.

Mary Jane travelled to the Crimea.

Mary Jane Seacole became famous in Britain and she wrote the story of her life. How would you describe her?

These words might help you - **clever, unhappy, brave, kind, friendly.**

Mary Seacole was ________________ and ________________.

Neil Armstrong

What do you know about Neil Armstrong?
Cross out the words which are not correct.

Neil Armstrong was an [architect] [astronaut.]

Neil Armstrong came from [America] [Russia.]

Neil Armstrong flew with [two] [three] other astronauts.

Neil Armstrong travelled in a spacecraft called
[Apollo 11] [Apollo 13.]

What do you think made Neil Armstrong famous?______________________

____

____

Cross out the statements which are not important in making him famous.

Neil Armstrong was a pilot.

Neil Armstrong was an astronaut.

Neil Armstrong was the first person to walk on the moon.

Neil Armstrong was a man.

Helen Sharman

What do you know about Helen Sharman?
Cross out the words which are not correct.

Helen Sharman was a school | teacher | scientist.

When Helen Sharman answered the advertisement | 30 | 1300 | people applied for the job.

Helen Sharman went to | America | Russia | to train to be an astronaut.

Helen Sharman stayed in space for | eight | eighty | days.

What do you think made Helen Sharman famous? ______________________

____

____

Cross out the statements which are not important in making her famous.

Helen Sharman learnt Russian.

Helen Sharman was an astronaut.

Helen Sharman was the first Briton in space.

Helen Sharman was a woman.

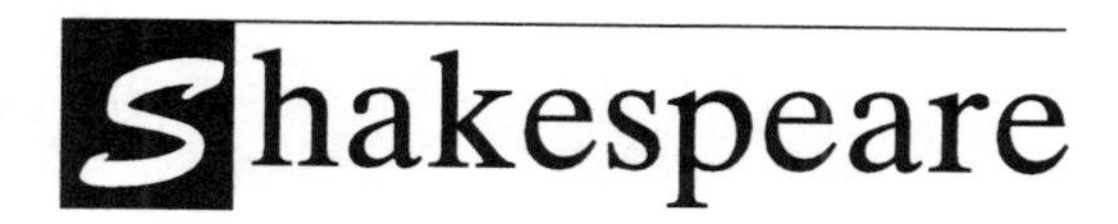

Shakespeare

These statements tell us something of Shakespeare's life.

Can you draw pictures to match the statements.

Shakespeare married Anne Hathaway.

Shakespeare was an actor in London.

Shakespeare was born in Stratford-upon-Avon. His father was a glove maker.

Shakespeare wrote many plays for the theatre

Shakespeare became famous in Britain and his plays are still performed. How would you describe him? These words might help you - **clever, unhappy, brave, kind, friendly, lonely**.

Shakespeare was ____________________

and ______________________________.

Roald Dahl

What do you know about Roald Dahl?
Cross out the words which are not correct.

Roald Dahl was a writer | train driver.

Roald Dahl was a pilot in World War I | World War II.

Roald Dahl wrote for television | newspapers.

Roald Dahl wrote a book called The Enormous Crocodile | Worry Warts.

What do you think made Roald Dahl famous? ________________

____

____

Cross out the statements which are not important in making him famous.

Roald Dahl was a pilot.

Roald Dahl was an author of children's books.

Roald Dahl lived in America.

Roald Dahl was a man.

Transporting Goods

Put the pictures in the correct order on this timeline.

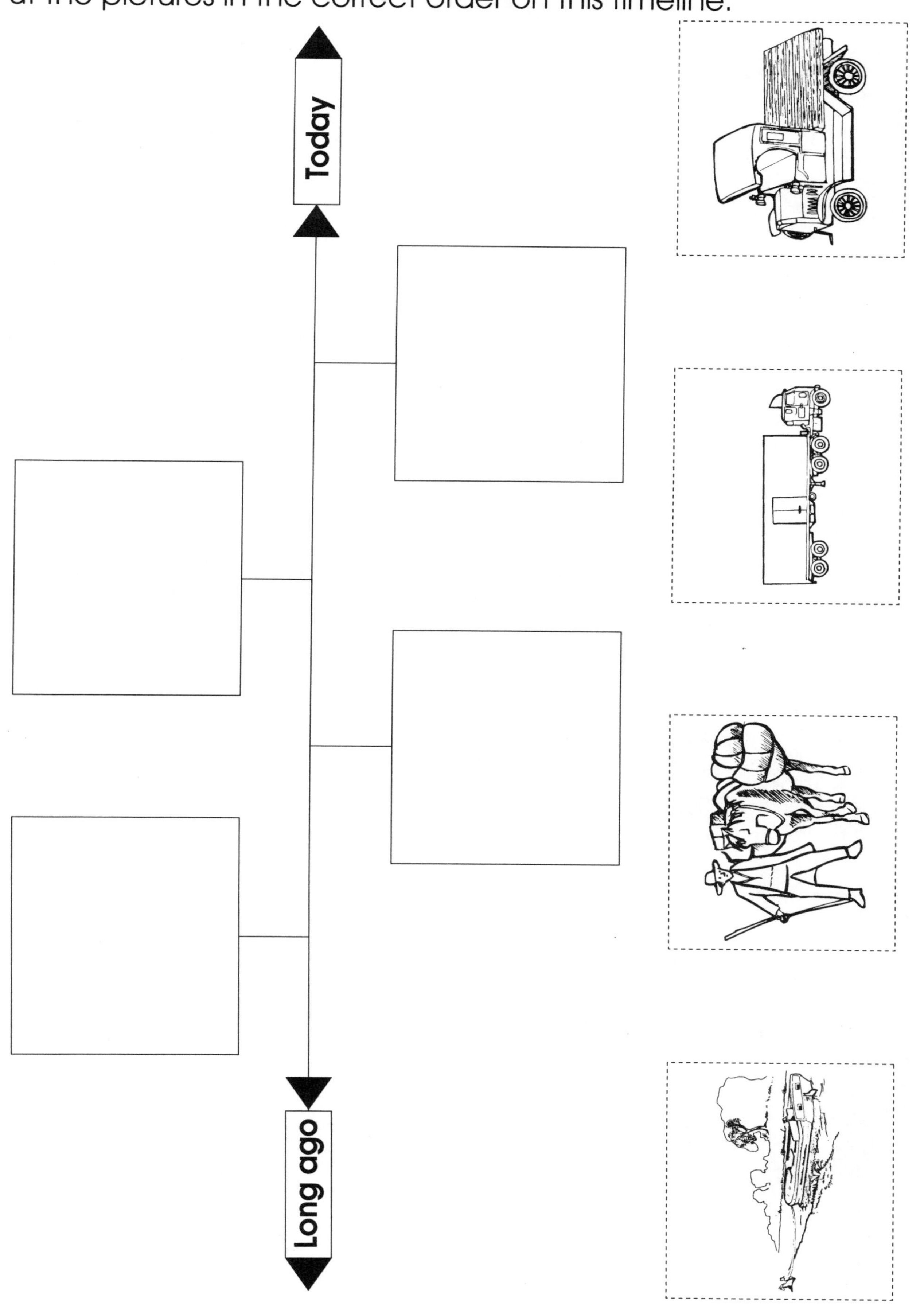

Transporting People

Put the pictures in the correct order on this timeline.

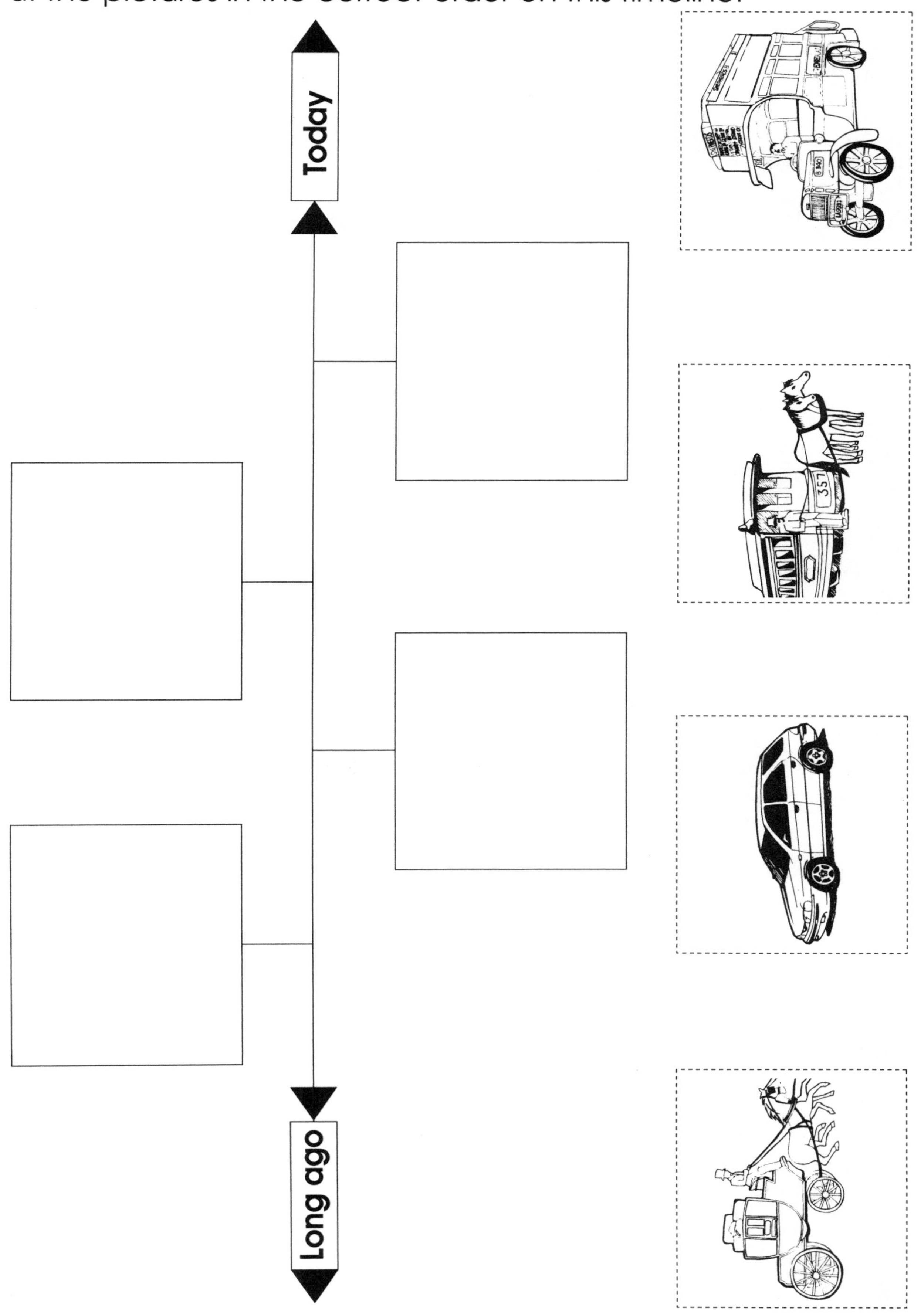

People Timeline

Put the pictures in the correct order on this timeline.

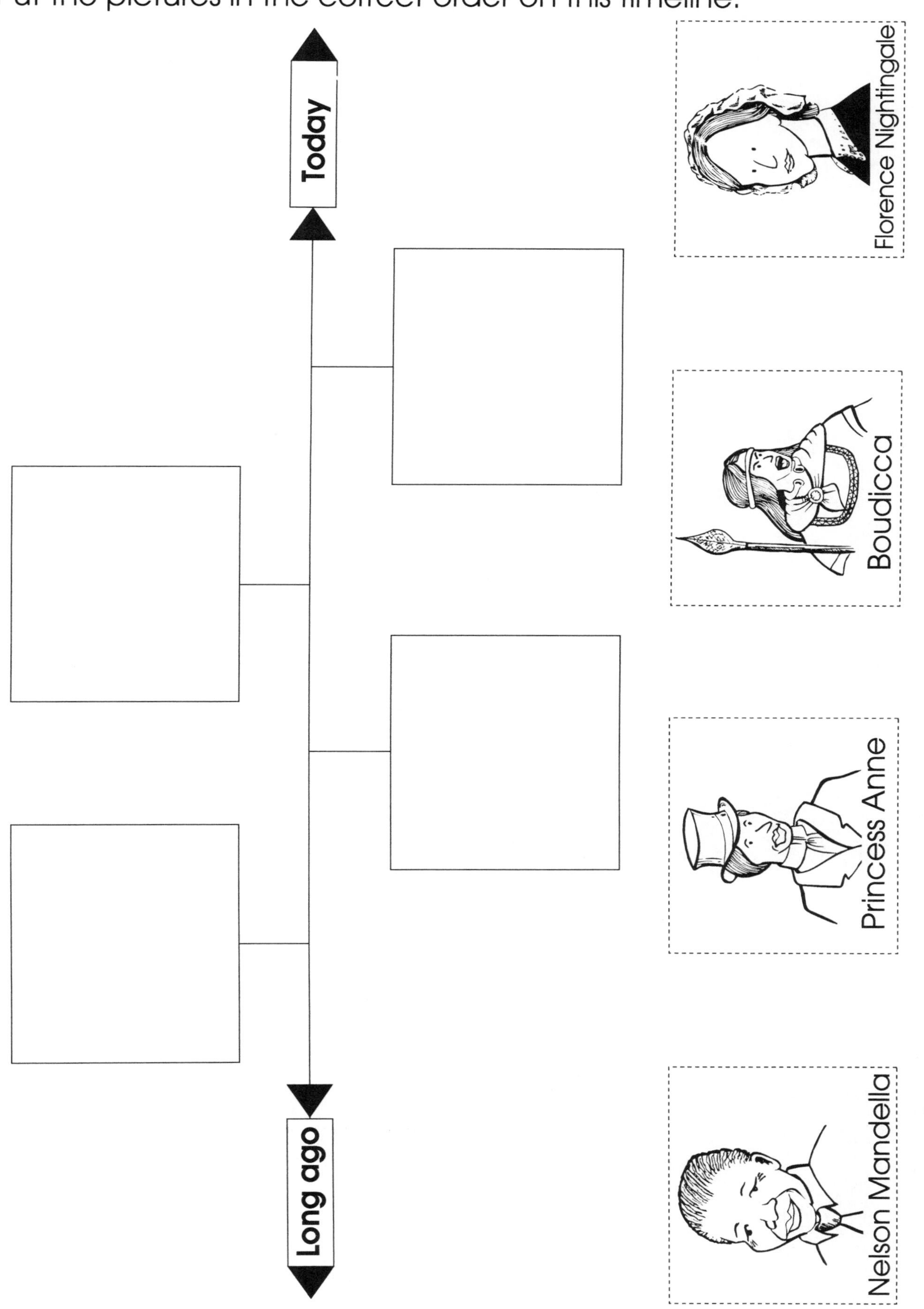

The Olympic Games

Which of these sports are played in the modern Olympic Games?

Which were played in the ancient Olympic Games?

Put an 'm' or an 'a' in each box.